C000151489

MODERN TOSS X

*from *hitflap*

by Jon Link & Mick Bunnage

Modern Toss: PO Box 386, Brighton BN13SN, United Kingdom
First printed up in the year 2017 ISBN: 978-0-9929107-6-1
Some of these cartoons first appeared in Private Eye Magazine.
A CIP catalogue record for this book is available from the British Library
Visit moderntoss.com to read more about all our books and to buy them yeah?
You will also find lots of other shit there, and you can sign up to the mailing list so you're
always first to hear about our releases. Cheers.

© modern toss 2017

injury workshop

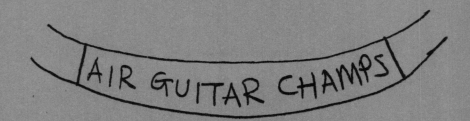

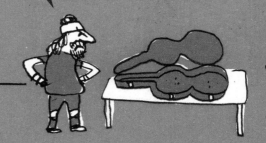

awkward cunt

would you like any bread or olives while you're waiting?

you tell me, it's your fucking restaurant

job interview

the shitshank redemption

binge watcher

saliva sample

I want to book a full DNA profile to confirm I'm definitely their mother

intergalactic arsehole hunter

meeting

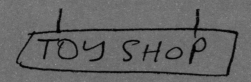

historical
shitter

I'd give that a couple of minutes if I were you

arse bailiff

hello we've come to repossess
your buttock implants

legal longshots

borrowed me mate's crane to do a bungee jump pop-up event, trying to a get a bit of cash together for me holiday, didn't have time to measure the rope, 200 foot of slack on the first bloke, fucker hit the car park floor like a tonne of shit, what are me options? fucked if i'm gonna jeopardise me holiday by dishing out refunds

leave it with me mate, don't let this spoil your trip

jazz salesman

retail

this food's dangerously out of date

yeah that's why it's a bit cheaper you fussy cunt

theoretical conspiricist

you know this whole thing was a hoax
staged by the government of the time

yeah check the shadow
on that corner flag

team player

olden days night out

Drive-by Abuser
considers
Walking a Dog

You walking a dog yeah?
gotta let it out 'int ya
fucking sniffs a lot don't it
every two fucking steps
oh it's having a piss now
remember your shit bags?
don't want to pay a 500 quid fine
for a bit of shit that you
didn't even technically do
catch you later yeah.

liberty taker

pop punt

terms & conditions

architecture

generation arsehole

I normally home tutor for maths GCSE

we just want you to train him not
to piss all round the toilet seat

medieval legend

Drive-by Abuser
considers
People Saying Sorry

Alright, you just said sorry to someone
'cos they bumped into you?
you need to recalibrate your
response to shit like that yeah?
what you gonna do if they punch you in the face?
offer to cook their fucking dinner or something?
sorry mate, I'm only joking
it's a fucking minefield yeah?
see you 'round.

sorry

musical prize evening

BRIT
AWARDS
2017

next up, the award for best lump of vaguely feel-good acoustic
hippy noodling used in a faceless multinational bank ad

dinner party

emojiency situation

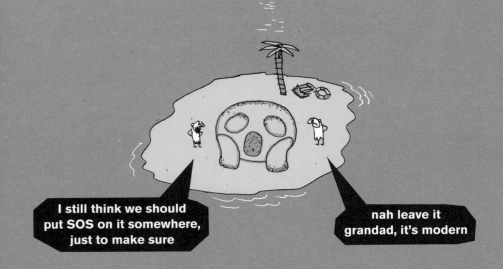

legal longshots

got a new set of super low frequency speakers yeah. testing 'em out in me garden, neighbours having a barbecue celebrating their kid's christening, they reckon the bottom end frequency made 'em all start shitting themselves, one bloke turned up on me doorstep with his guts in a carrier bag. on the plus side channel 5 have signed me up for an episode of their 'arsehole neighbours' franchise

excellent news, that'll be a great shop window for your talents, i'll make sure you secure a decent slab of any box set receipts

homework

books

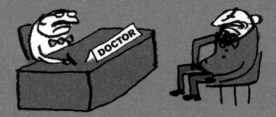

health

marketing

yeah, what we really need is a single gesture marketing initiative that maximises customer awareness and consolidates foolery for the emerging international markets
what about some random made up day of the year to celebrate pranks and general titting about?
I've got a window around the start of April?
I could get a mead brewer in to sponsor it
ties in perfectly with the mushroom season, everyone'll be pranked off their nut

legal longshots

rented out a victorian steam roller, fuckers in the shop never told me where the handbrake was, popped down the garden centre to buy some slug pellets, flattened half the main outbuilding while trying to manoeuvre into a parking space, cop shop reckons i'm looking at six points on me licence and a multiple manslaughter charge, plus i'm fucked if me insurance is going up just cos of this

leave it with me, i should be able to copy and paste a load of shit from an identical case involving a bloke with a wrecking ball

blue plaque committee

Pete Peters
Vigilante Shit Stirrer

hello yeah I want to speak to someone about selling some of my personal data...

mostly detailed info on me moving about my house, what room I'm in at specific times of the day, what book I'm reading when I'm having a shit, you get the fucking picture...

anyway get someone to call me back and we can put whatever procedures we need in place and get the ball rolling...

my phone number? yeah that's coming out at 20 quid cash per digit, plus the international code, think of it as a signing on fee. No, I can't leave my name, I haven't priced that up yet, ok yeah well fuck you too.

trade off

smart bin

arsehole surgery

voter brain capture

I'm prepared to give you full time for your cooperation. stand up on the condition you follow up a much m annoying stupid fucking name from I

lastly, how did you hear about us?

dunno, I think I was psychologically targeted via social media?

smart arse

hyper-banterisation

what's happening?

Mr Tourette

MASTER SIGNWRITER

I need a sign to get sponsors interested in funding my charity road trip holiday down to the south of France. If there's any cash left over after I've paid for all my food and drink I'll give it to a charity which will be decided by a vote on twitter

that's a complex fucking message you're trying to get over, I'll try and boil it down

Later...

FREE LOADING CUNT RACKET

fucking hell glad I'm not paying for that

It's on the house as long as you promise to use it

cheese&wine

this is Roger who runs a short story workshop

email me all the details so I don't go by accident

liberty taker

awkward cunt

THE FRIENDS OF MODERN TOSS

WE VALUE YOUR PATRONAGE

Catherine Cluett, ESQUISHY MCSQUISHFACE, Shaun Corkerry, "Pery Hunt, Yeah?", Jack Basey, Naomi Joslin-Tan, Al Wood, Mac, John de Pear, Tim Mingewards, Leigh Bollocks, Phil Williams, Spike Moody, Luke Miller, Peter Wormald, David-I want pecs like Wahlberg-Danks, "Patto, the whitest man this size of Greenland", Alison Poo Face, Old School ST, Gaz custody Worley, Geraint Rogers, Robin Woodward, Snebular Wankboy Jones, *LIL' KELS & SAM SPACEY*, Chris fucking Dorward, Dee Thunderbird Johnson, Justyn Herbert, Simon Belly Wash Arnold, Andy&Becky Fisher-Shaw, Dave Smith, Louise Scullion, Jamie Strachan, Steven McDade, Neil "Utter Cunt" Colman, Spanner Snakes, Chris Westwood, Jenny Bird, James Tuhey, Dave Mason, Vinni and Vic Van Diesel, Helen Comben, Kim Hunt, Charlotte Adams, Blondie & Babba Gobbin, Ellie Delbaere, Karen Karras, Don Nicholass-McKee, William Nicholass-McKee, Julia Edwards, Barry Simner, Gilly Williamson, Charles Michael Silvey, Wetpants Wetjen, Dan 'Safest Hands' Small, BOB MCLEAN, GRACEISACE Harris-Johnson, Paul Duggan, Graham Smith, Sean Furness, Alex Robinson, Jake Zak, Anu Ralhan, Simon "Shitpeas" Childs, Tim "Thunderpussy" Taylor, David "Growler" Gregson, Martin "Mum Botherer" Cowie, MJ&LT for ever, Onwards to Chamonix!, Dr Rachel MacLean, Claire Tulley, Katie Atkinson, Alfie & Daddy Moss Vale, Mr Lacey, HittMan, Jake Zak, FUCK YOU PAUL CONNAH, Scott Fucking Harris, Michael "Hurdy Gurdy" F., Jessica Skangar Henderson, Dickie & Shelly S. Grethe, Toby Miarka, Matt Baywatch, Michael Key, Richard Ashdown, Dave Guy, Verity Rose, Gary Brooks, Stewart Nolan, Jeremy Bryant, Jeremy Smith, Iain Milne, Steve Smithard, Stephen Lorimer, ROB (A CUNT) MCNEILL, MR P, Anne Esler, SELTAX, Claire Doris Davey, Mark Keegan, Simon Pinner, Lee Barlow, Ada and Emmeline Chelms, Rich and Hannah Doran, Fuckin looks like it Clarke, sickBocks, Paul 'Godlike' Goodwin, Chris "r u ok hun?" Ko, Tamara Young 4 James Rowe, RPJ - Alone Again..., Ignatius J. O'Reilly, Westy, Rich Kew, Phil Philcox, Dario Canale, _A´_£_$, Tall Dog, Hero the hedgehog, Steve Cooke, Andrew 'Cockchops' Wynne, Big Les, Layla Cunting Bensiali, J. Grosvenor-Smoots Esq., Fraser Neasham, Kate Villalgordo, Tom Skidmore, Jason loves Emma Swan, *STRUMSKI*, £2.60 delivery? Arseholes, Gavin Willerton, Rona Hunnisett, Shitehawk McGonadplums, Dennis Fox, Patrick Spragg, "gamingdave" Robinson, Fraser Neasham, Ben 'tiny nipples' Johnson, Soapy Purvez, ktaitch, Charley Butters, MARK AND CLIVE, RICH PARSONS, Rob Ford, Oliver Dentaaaaay Booth, Mat Eames, Ivan, Trevor Sims, Snorgemeister, Carey Harrison-Allan, Flumpy Fuckin' Florko, Mrs Roisin Joynson, Chris Knowles, Winchy, Patrick Fuller, Rob 'Bulldog' Mackay, Fletcher Smiths, Ben Golding, Tommo, Karolina Bywater, Mark Horsfield, Liam Tulett, Ross, Catherine, Richard Brown, Dave Spencer, Paul Gregson, Elliot James, Ben Finn, Bob Rattray, Marie "MAJORIE!!!" King, Stephen J "Peas" King, Barney Russel, Anna whitby, DEWIE, The Wonderful Mr Exelby, boc chris, Michael Glasper, Phil Ball, Mathew Edwards, Drew Swinerd, Crum Pett, Phil Piss-Weasel Hines, Charlie Wise, Sarah Wilsdon, Peter Moore, Brendan Giuseppe Smart, Benjamin Luigi Nagel, Robert Dawes MEng, Mr David "Huge" Hughes, Sophie Fucking Greenwood, Tim Hillman-Brown, Ian & Cath, Neil Patience, "oi mate, you Marc?", Dave Vollans, James Forbes, Benbenbenbenben, Milton Waddams, Tom Sirignano, DAVE THE GRAVE, M S Lawson MBE, Vita Ruby, Andy the Corpse Tickler, JONATHAN KNOWLES, JACK LOWE, Ian and Jennie, Annie Divver, Chris Mills, Matty Pee, Andrew Carlin, "Willy G", Jonny H, Doug Moreno Cunt!, Phokus, MoonBoysofBuxtonRoad, GRAEME STEWART, Richard Vincent-Spall, Laura'19yrs of this toss', Gary Thomas Ball, Testo & Crapper, Mark Leftly, "Dan & Sarah Harrison, yeah", BlockersnotLockers, Alex Head, Anthony Barton, Tedwidge Waterfield, DJMastrBaish & MCPNusLenz, David Frettsome, Pidermite Underground, Dougie Wands, Nick Jagger, Grinxtrel Print, Charlie Easterbrook, I WILL BE GIRL G LUX, Will Grove-Merritt, KEITH "THE FUCKING BOSS!", Tina Anobile, WOOHOO IanPaulMarsh, Roberto (BOB) Titmus, Big Stu Goode, x casper jt scrivener x, Liz Clark, Max Awkward-Cunt esq, Richard Alden, Saul Underemployed Taylor, Nick Winter, Colonel Chinstrap, Maria & Adam Dare, Rhodri Hunter-James, Simon Hardwick, Mark Himsworth, GriffMate, That git Mark Linton, David Cameron, DUSTY DOOZY, Ben Halliwell, Knightsypops, jason barlow, David Blakey & Anna Adam, Roger Cunting Mullis, Antony and Julia Silson, Joel Nesbitt, jason tynan, "Stuart Hatcher, yeh?", STINKY PUMPS, Nick TWINK Addison, Bryan "B-Ry" Richardson, John Roofrack, SIR MILES PATERSON OBE, Anthony Peters, Ian "Dobber" Dobson, Adam Stanborough, Dave Taylor, Edie & Zandig Mason, Dave Hollander, Julie Jones, Bobby Pegg, Alabama Love Nash, BIG JEZ, Mary, Philippa Fenner, Maris Soonsein, Colin the Beast, peteamour, Jamie Keddie, Kevin Sloane, Drew Wilkes, Ian Morley, Steve Collins, Quasi Bill Lynch, Mr Tiberius Reese, ***** MIKE ASHWORTH *****, Keith Cooke, Joe Warwick, Sarah Watt, Tony bone, Daz Quayle, Robin Fucktard Fulford, Shitty Von Blurt Ass, Christopher Moore, Tich Critchlow, S J "Shit Butler" Hayward, Mark Harman, Anthony Richard Adams, Mark Harforth, W.I.F.A, DFR, Le Ginge, Mij n Lainy, Cayly Bolton, Sweetshop, Mickey, Paul Clark, David Harrison, Rudie Todd, Si & Angel Jones, Councillor McFee, Lloyd Stanton, Bladderwrack, Andy T, Val Ellis, Andy Anthrax, Simon C, Phil Greenhalgh, Rory Jackson, Malcolm "Jim" Morrison, Guy O'Keefe, Jim Binning, JoJoJu Edgson, JIM CLEAR, Lewis Bradley, Douglas Karnaj, Gary Grice, Simon Brownpants, Kev And Sara McCready, Clive Fucking Moys, Deirdre Maguire, Fiona Hedderman, Alfie Dean, Jem Jedrzejewski, Anne darling Faith Hook, "johnnyapples", Margaret Thompson, Darren Hubbard, Freda Mary Russell Davies, Sally Cotts, Eve Luke Elsi FerryBodder, Cunty McCuntface, Joe Reynolds, PAUL S J MARTIN, PAUL JACKMAN, Russ "Bonzoconkers" Dean, Abigail Walker, Anne "3.1" Maningas, Wagon McWheel, Neal Cresswell, Matt Jo Florence Flynn Hook, Steph Watts, Eryl Price, Will, Woody, Geoffy, Julian Wakeley, Emma Chisit, Ellie Wells, MIKE STAFFORD IN CAPITALS, Mark Evans, Steve Carter, Fish Monkey, Rob Fucking Halloway, Boaby Driver, Paul Marray, Ginge Kirwan, Beccy Griffiths, Andrew Dawson, Jane LSP x, TimboHavzy, THE CASA MIRTH PODCAST, Hog-Face Hicks the Paedo, The GMC Cunts, Richard The Cunt Clifford, Stephen Davison, Cath and Stu, John Huke, Johnnie Tonota, Conrad Bennett, Tom Price, Matt Blackler, Pug_Presley, Alison Walster yeah, Michael Gove, The cunts at Cunt Cottage, Euan McDonald, Edwin Graham, HomoMilitia U.K., LucianAndAmberAngelWilliam, Mike Purnell, James Smith fae Elgin, Gary Fucking Sharpe, Fabian Breckels, Pete FUCK ME Gaskill, John CUNT CHOPS Guzzardi, Michael Hannan, Kerry Shittin' Herdman, Matt Lander, Mark Ayton, Prof. J. Wilson, Claire 'Furs' Fursey, "Joe & Sam Wicks, yeah?", RHIANNON HOLLICK-COOPER, Dave Blackman, Robin Blackwell, Ben "The Dutchman" Brown, Stephen Potter, Samantha Tang, Richard Midwinter yeah, *Sarah & Pauly Surridge*, Barry Antoinette, Nick Patch, Pamela Glennie, Lord Tiggington, Neil Todd, John Ritchie, Miten M, NEIL&VICKY, Howard Greenwood, Spendo & Charmaine, theholyllama, Chris Plumley, Edric Ellis, Antony Medley, Dave Johnson, Anne Eleanor Steve CURRAN, Simon "Shitpeas" Childs, Anthony, Alex Nghhaaaaaargh, "Rob Caunt with an a, yeah", Adrian Sheehan, @nickleics, ROBERT DOWNIE, MIKE & MICHAEL KING GOMEZ, Bjorn Christensen, Mr Gareth A Jones, Jon Bates, Dr. Alan Bennett, Christine Syred, DOOZY'S DINER, Jani Gunn, "Tom Smith, yeah?", Brendan Horan, Bill Grindlay, Jon... that ginger cunt, Simon "Dentaaaay" Fenn, Darren Gaskell, Chris Holt, Mick Hare Dom Liddell, Mark Stent, Steve 'Teddy' Evans, JAMES TWEEDIE YEAH!!!!!, Jon 'Dave's Bro' Goodwin, Richard Wilsdon, Fuck You Paddy, ADAM MAD DOG WATERS, <Insert Clever Name Here>, Joey, Gareth Mason, Dr Bob Reece KBE, Katy Dyer, Michael Cole, Edward 'Tedd' Mills, Andrew Dickface Tebbenham, Rupert Cunty Frog Stone, Gary Kurt McConnell, Allister Frost, Martin Ruddy, Crump!, Robin "BARNSTORMER", Andrew J Fox, Eduardo Levi Suarez, Idwell Levi Parry Jones, Darreb Levi Mibbleton, Ian 'HUMPTY' Humphreys, BEN ROWE, Nick Reilly, Neil Elkins, STEVe PAPe, ASKY, Darrell Hannam, rudespoons, Michael Bryant, TB, Stuart Wilson, Jo "Troth Monster" Troth, J Arthur, DikieBoyC, Steve P...yeah?, Meester Bond, Gambo the Cunt, Ant 'Adidas' Maude, @mrnickharris, Eoin O'Connor, Gareth Barton, Jonah, Jeffrey Worrall, Neil "Fifteen" Conner, Myriam Ellis, "Aaz Shitnak Brown, yeah?", Nick & Dave Baldacci, DinoKatie, Jon Gregory, Mutha Fucka Chris Tucker, Felix & Jasper Minion, Kunt, Jake Cunt!, Ricky the Chicken, Gary "Fuck IKEA!!", Derek Bell, Charleen Eade, Lionel Hives, Wolfy Ryan, Ed Johnston, Tall' Paul Roberts, Graham Ward, Jonny Hall & Jonny Bongo, John Fahy, The Metcalves, Andrea Parker, Tooney & Tooney 2, AKATOMBO, Jon Lister, Andy Southcombe, Mr Jonathan Curtis Miller, Matthew Alexander Kaufman, Rona Hunnisett, Ivan Meel of Divus, Antoni Georg, Matthew Keen, Iain 'Bone Cank' Lockey, STEVE MATTHEWS, mr. christopher e holden, Arnauld 'Le cunt' Robin, Jim Allen, "RHYS LIGHTNING, YEAH?", Flying Dutchman, Stephen Cuntard Martin, "Dr Anna "knees" Wheeler", Simon King, ALAN YOU WANKER, MARCUS THE KIWI, Martin Watson, Chris Huddleston, Chris Baldwin, Little Bea, Aaron Taylor-Cotter yeah?, Richard Mallett, Stewart Killala, Matt Lucock, Darren Startup, Iain 'Wilbossman' Wilson, "Adam ""no filth please"" Croney", Martin Brown, steveindisguise, Brett Sanderson, Lord C'unty Jim, PORTSLADE DAVE YEAH, Richard Jenner, Steve Townsend, Moving Jim, Finch Fletcher, Mike Byrne, Brian White-McCunty, Gary Hughes, Robert Cunting Silkstone, Andrew Turner, Gareth Gamble, Alex Fraser, Saisage fingers Tyler, ELTON LAM, SERENITY NOW, DOPSKOP, Ross Neary, Ben Neary, Jez Burn, Andrew Sturgis, DB, Charlotte Cook, Captain Billy Firebeard, Dan Rebellato, Marcus Tustin, Kevin A(Arsebiscuit) Whie, Rupert Henson, Dara Maguire, Keith 'MongPorn.com' Dean, Nigel 'ShitTits.com' Grif, PBG, olivier robin, "Nick Kenny, Simon Fox", Reverend Ram Rod Tod, Ed Boucher, Tom Walston, Mr Neil The-Hippy, "Dave, Karen, Lily and Annie High", The Joe-Jo Collective, Alex Lawson, Peter Johnson, Mike Johnson, Bov, John Kyle, Mangrove, Jim Christian, Martin Wright, Mr Thomas Redpath esq, John Dobson, JAMES M.D. MOSELY ESQ., Matt ""Dicko"" Dixon", nobhead, "Tom ""badger, I love Taity"" White", Mrs Jake Cushion-Plumper, Lizard Farrington, Fretworker, "Steve Potz-Rayner, again", ~BOB PULLEN~, Paul 'Pissflaps' Porter, Notned Mothpools, Mark Platt, Monty you terrible cunt, Steggs and Lisa, Garrison Du Ponci©, Florence & Tigger, Johney de Wunderful, Phil Sherer, Simon Hyland, Sarah Nash's Bump, Guy Breuer, Hagrid, KEVIN 'CIDER I UP' LOWRIE, Lord Gavin Thompson, Ken Horse, Robin Palmer, Matt Morden, Sean Taplin, DOUG FUCKING LAZY, Pierre Mansel, CRUCIAL 'ZINE, Robin Palmer, Kristian Horwood, Elizabeth Hite, Paul J, Simon Niemiec, McKnight, Jamie fucking Hancock, Richard Pedrick, James Dougall, "Steve ""you horror"" Wrench", Stefan Jaworzyn, Mr & Mrs Fat Knackers, Matthew 'Jizzy' Butcher, Sanil 'Linus' Gautama, Aaron Newman, Steve Wernick, Lee Turnock, Andy 'Bottle O' Piss' Fernandez.